BILAL IBN RABAH

From Darkness into Light

translated by Sara Saleem

Published by

Ta-Ha PUBLISHERS Ltd.
1, Wynne Road
LONDON SW9 0BB

© Copyright Ta-Ha Publishers Ltd. 1405/1984

Reprinted: 1992, 1995, 1998

Published by:
Ta-Ha Publishers Ltd.
1, Wynne Road
London SW9 OBB
website:http://www.taha.co.uk/
email: sales@taha.co.uk

British Library Cataloguing in Publication Data
Saleem, Sara
    Bilal Ibn Rabah - From Darkness into Light - 2nd ed
    1. Islam - History
    I. Title
    297. 63

ISBN 0 907 461 84 0

Printed and Bound by: *De-Luxe Printers,*
London NW10 7NR.
website: http://www.de-luxe.com
email: printers@de-luxe.com

CONTENTS

1 IN THE NAME OF ALLAH, THE MOST MERCIFUL, THE MOST GRACIOUS.

Night approached and the stars glittered brightly in the sky. The stifling heat of the day gradually began to recede, bringing in its place the humidity of the night. Everywhere, the people heaved sighs of relief. The day had been unbearably hot, It was as if all hell had been let loose, showing its secrets to mankind so that they would remember it and fear its punishment and the the terror of its flames. It was as if it wanted to remind them of their wasted lives and make them reflect upon the idols they worshipped besides Allah, even though they had never seen them perform any miracle or display any power. In fact they had never done anything beneficial at all.

The people were now smiling and happy. A man commented to his companion, "What a beautiful night this is, and how close we were today to death, only the night with its fragrant air and moist breeze has saved us."

Now at this very moment, in the houses of the Bani Jomah, a man from the highest and noblest tribe was sitting with his family and his wives. He was heavily built and his features indicated that he was a harsh, severe man, yet also of cowardly character. The man called out,

"Bilal . . . Bilal!" The slave hurried towards him. He was black in colour, delicately built, tall and slim, with a narrow face and a slight beard. His hair was thick.

"Yes, Master," he replied.

"Bring us our evening meal."

"Straight away, Master." The slave hurried away from his master's sight.

After the people had eaten and drunk to their fill, they sat, talking into the night about whatever took their fancy. The hours passed one by one until it was almost the middle of the night, and the people went to rest their tired and weary bodies. Bilal waited until they were all asleep. His eyelids had become very heavy, so he finally submitted to sleep. The entire tribe was soon overtaken by a deep slumber.

As the night passed, Bilal turned over on his mat. He was sleeping lightly and he opened his eyes As he did not see anything, he again closed them, giving in to an all-encompassing and delightful sleep. It was only a few minutes later that Bilal again opened his eyes. He thought that he had heard a voice calling him, as if in a dream. He rose from his mat, listening carefully. Presently, he heard a voice calling him softly, as if it was coming from inside a grave:
"Bilal . . . Bilal! . . ."

Bilal jumped up in fright, seized with a strange sensation. He hurried to open the door, his thoughts scattered and diffused. Gently, he half opened the door, and streching his neck, he caught a glimpse of a vertical figure in the darkness. Its shape was thin,with slender legs. The face was white and gaunt, with a slight growth of beard and sunken eyes.

"Who is it?" Bilal called out.

"Abu Bakr."

"Abu Bakr! What brings you here at this hour?"

"Something very important; I have to tell you about it straight away."

"Would it not have been better to wait until morning?"

"No, Bilal. . .The reason I have come now is so that I can tell you while we are far from people's prying eyes."

"How strange you are Abu Bakr! Anyway, say what you will. All shall be well by the will of Allah."

"Listen, Bilal. Do you remember the time you came with us on the trading mission of the Qureish, to Syria?"

"Yes, I remember."

'And do you also recall the day you came with me to see the monk there, and you told him of a vision you had seen. He told us that one day a Prophet would appear in the land of the Arabs?"

"Yes. . .I remember it well."

"Well, the prophecy of the monk has been fulfilled, Bilal. The Prophet of this nation has indeed appeared."

"The Prophet of this nation?"

"Yes, yes, Bilal!"

"But who is he?"

"Muhammad, son of Abdullah, son of Abdul Muttalib."

"But Abu Bakr . . . how do you know that he really is the Prophet?"

"I heard a rumour coming from Makkah, saying that Muhammad had secretly begun to call people to proclaim the Unity of the One God, and I knew that this was indeed the truth. So I went to see him and asked him,

"O Abu'l Qasem, what is this I hear about you?" He replied, "What have you heard about me, O Abu Bakr?" I said to him, "I have heard that you are preaching the Unity of Allah and are claiming to be the Prophet of Allah." At this he replied, "O Abu Bakr, my Lord Who is Mighty and Exalted, has made me a bringer of good Tidings and a Warner. He has entrusted me with the work of Ibrahim, and has sent me to all mankind." Then I told him, "By Allah, I have never known you to lie, you are truly qualified for Prophethood by your honesty, your exemplary behaviour and your good deeds. Therefore I acknowledge you as the Prophet of Allah." The Prophet then held out his hand and I took it, pledging allegiance."

"This is the strangest story I have ever heard O Abu Bakr, but tell me, what is it that Muhammad is inviting us to?"

"He is calling us to worship Allah, The Creator of the Heavens and the Earth and all that lies between them. There is no god but He, Lord of the Mighty Throne, The Knower of our innermost selves, The Observer of all that we do, The Rewarder and Punisher of all deeds - good for good and bad for bad."

"What does Muhammad ask us to do?"

"He calls us to worship Allah alone and this call, O Bilal, is the call to Truth, Justice and Equality. It teaches us that all men are as equal as the teeth of a comb, and says that a free man is no better than a slave, nor a slave better than a free man, except by virtue of his Faith (Iman) and his Righteousness (Taqwa). By Allah, Bilal, I want only what is best for you; believe in this; do not hesitate. The invitation of Muhammad leads to happiness, beyond which there is no happiness and to good above which there is no good. O Bilal, say: "There is no god but Allah and Muhammad is the Messenger of Allah."

At these words, Bilal became silent and bowed his head, gazing at the ground. Then he lifted it, looked at Abu Bakr, and said in a calm, gentle voice, "I bear witness that there is no god but Allah and I bear witness that Muhammad is the Messenger of Allah."

Bilal's embracing of Islam made Abu Bakr very happy and his face shone with delight. He said, "Tomorrow we will go to Muhammad and I will wait for you at this hour in my house. Do not be late!"

"I won't, Abu Bakr."

Abu Bakr shook Bilal's hand, clasping it, and then set off back home.

Bilal, the weak slave, who had no power or authority, no high position or dominion, had proclaimed his faith by pronouncing the two Shahadas. He did not yet know that his submission was to bring painful punishment and severe persecution, inflicted on him by the high ranking men of Makkah, those who were allured by the worldly life and who were satisfied with the life of this earth. They feared that Muhammad's message would bring them down from their high positions and would remove the distinction between slave and master. They did not realize that the tables would soon be turned and that this weak slave would become an honoured man, recorded in history on proud and glorious pages. For generations and centuries to come, his name would live on throughout time until the Day of Judgement.

After having accepted Islam, Bilal would hear people saying; "Bilal and servants like him, only believe in Muhammad's message because they see it as a great benefit for themselves. They think it will make them equal with the rest of the tribe and with their masters. But what is the use of this teaching for the rest of the people and for their leaders? What is the point of lowering themselves to the position of their slaves?"

No. . .The companions of the Prophet,(may Allah bless him and grant him peace), whether they were free men or slaves, believed only because they felt that the Truth had filled their hearts and was pushing them strongly towards Faith in Allah, The Merciful, The Compassionate.

The slaves did not believe simply because Islam made them equal with free men, nor did free men believe because Islam made them equal with slaves. The benefit of such a policy would only apply at the most to a mere section of the population. Both slaves and free men believed because deep in their hearts they longed to worship Allah, and because deep in their hearts they longed to live in the Garden of the next world.

There is a big difference between having Faith and seeking material gain. They stem from two totally different sources. The seeking of material gain is something which accompanies a person's life or a part of it. Faith is everlasting; it transcends the single person and in its path he surrenders all desire for material gain and even life itself, since he knows that the next life is the home that lasts forever.

3   ALLAH IS ONE

Bilal, now that he was a Muslim by the grace of Allah, used to visit the house of the Prophet Muhammed,(may Allah bless him and grant him peace), from time to time, in the still of the night or in the evening. Once, when he came back from visiting the Prophet,(may Allah bless him and grant him peace), Bilal was struck with the idea of walking around the Ka'aba, to look at the strange idols that had

11

been placed in and around it by the idol worshippers, to see what effect they would have on him, now that he had embraced Islam.

The first idol he saw was called Hubl. It was huge in width and stature and reckoned to be the mightiest and most powerful of all the idols. It was made of carnelian red stone, and had the face of a man. Its right hand had been broken and the people had replaced it with one of solid gold. No one knew exactly how its hand had been broken, or when or where, but it was thought that someone had broken it off one night and taken it home to derive blessings.

Bilal looked at the idol and found it just as it was before; it had not moved so much as an inch. He continued looking at it for a while, then burst out laughing. "Did I really worship this idol?" he thought. "What did I really see in it worthy of being worshipped? I really must have been blind."

Bilal thought he would defy the chief idol, so he lifted his hand and slapped it on its face as hard as he was able, and waited to see what it would do. The idol however, did not budge and Bilal reckoned that the great idol had perhaps delegated the task of revenge to its offspring which surrounded it. He looked around him but saw that all the idols, without exception, were engrossed in deep slumber. There was nothing left for Bilal to do but to spit on the chief idol - and still it did nothing!

As Bilal was about to leave, he was unaware of the fact that he had been observed the whole time by a man, who had witnessed his every movement. He had seen him abusing the idol by hitting it and spitting on its face, all the while concealing his anger.

A new day dawned. The noblemen of the Qureish sat around the Ka'aba, talking, as they did on most mornings. This morning the conversation was heated and centred around Muhammad, (may Allah bless him and grant him peace), and his preaching. They had begun pondering over this sudden danger which was threatening to end their mastery and power. Whilst they were talking thus, they saw a man coming towards them in a great hurry. He sat down next to Ummayya Ibn Khalaf and whispered in his ear. The noblemen of the Qureish saw Ummayya's face turn from yellow to red and saw signs of anger appear on his face.

"Are you telling the truth?" he asked the man.

"Yes, I saw it with my own eyes".

"What did he do?"

"Something so terrible . . . I can't even bring myself to tell you."

"Speak, do not be afraid. Woe betide that insolent slave!"

13

"I saw him abusing the great idol, and then he . . . he . . spat in its face."

"My god! I will extract the mightiest revenge from this insolent slave. His impudence has really gone too far," exclaimed Ummayya furiously.

"I have also seen him going to see Muhammad in the middle of the night and sitting with him until daybreak."

"Alright, go now . . . and keep observing him secretly."

The elders of the Qureish looked at Ummayya, asking for an explanation. "What was that you were talking about?" they demanded.

"My slave, Bilal."

"What about him?"

"I had been hearing rumours for some time now, saying that he goes to see Muhammad during the night, so I sent someone to follow him. He came to me today informing me that the imudent slave has abused our idol and even spat in its face."

Abu Jahl spoke first, saying, "I fear that if we do not take steps to stop Muhammad's preaching while it is still in its early stages, ours will be a terrible lot. Listen Ummayya, go home now and discipline this ungreatful slave of yours. Teach him a harsh lesson that will serve warning to those who are thinking in their ugly hearts, of accepting the message of Muhammad,

"Yes," said Ummayya, "We'll teach him a lesson that will be the talk of all Makkah."

He rose from the group with an evil look in his eyes and hurried off.

Ummayya went inside his house and called for Bilal. When he approached, he said, "Do you think I don't know of your movements and where you go to every night? No, I know everything Bilal, so leave this religion which you have adopted and return to our religion; it is the best way."

But Bilal only replied, "No, By Allah, I will not renounce my faith, ever!"

"Bilal, obey me or I will pulverize you and tear you limb from limb," Ummayya threatened.

"I am not afraid of anyone but Allah, and I will certainly not give up my faith for anyone."

"Bilal, I will not argue any more with you. I will make you return to your old religion, by force if necessary."

"Do what you wish," Bilal replied.

Ummayya called his servants and helpers, then told them to dress Bilal in old rags and to tie a rope around his neck. Then he told them to call the children and servants of the area, and to tell them to pull Bilal through the streets.

As the children pulled Bilal along, everyone asked, "What is going on here?" They were told, "He has rejected the idols and the religion of our forefathers, and he follows the religion of Muhammad." The people then began pouring abuse on him and invoking the wrath of the idols upon him.

In the face of this ceaseless taunting, Bilal however, just kept crying out, as loud as he could, "One . . . One . . . One."

The children continued dragging Bilal from place to place all day long, until fatigue and exertion had taken a heavy toll on him.

Later that night, Ummayya Ibn Khalaf went to see Bilal. He went in good spirits, sure that the punishment would have produced the desired effect. Ibn Khalaf did not know however, that when a believer's heart is full of faith, it is unconquerable by any worldly power. Nothing can be detracted from it, nor can it be influenced in the slightest way.

"So, Bilal," Ummayya shouted, "perhaps now you will have come to your senses and will leave the religion of Muhammad?"

Bilal simply replied, "One . . . One . . . One . . ."

"forget all that Bilal, Muhammad can't save you from your punishment."

"One . . . One . . . One . . ."

Ummayya continued to punish Bilal, every day in a different manner. Bilal, however, patiently endured everything, determined to make these noblemen look foolish, and show just how ineffective their wealth and power were in the face of his strong belief.

During this time however, Ummayya's patience began to run out. He went to his friend, Abu Jahl, to ask if he should kill the slave.

Abu Jahl told him, "Don't kill the slave; by doing so you will only admit to our weakness. Look, I have an idea. Today, it is extremely hot . . . put Bilal in an armoured suit made of iron and shackle him in one of the flat areas of Makkah, under the burning sun. You will see him begging for mercy in no time."

"What a wonderful idea Abu Jahl," said Ummayya. "Also, I'll put a huge boulder on his chest."

Ummayya went off to see Bilal and shackled him in iron, under the torturous sun. On his chest, he placed a huge boulder, just as he had suggested to Abu Jahl. Then he looked straight at Bilal and said, "So, Bilal, how do you feel now, eh?"

Bilal simply replied as he had done previously, One . . . One . . . One . . ."

"Go on Bilal, repeat One, One, One," taunted Ummayya, "We will see how your One will help you. This punishment will continue until you either return to our religion or die."

"Even if you threaten to kill me," said Bilal, "I will not associate partners to Allah, merely out of fear of death."

Everyone who came to see Bilal was amazed at this slave who was prepared to suffer torture for the sake of his convictions.

Now, it so happened that Abu Bakr As-Siddiq was passing by on his way home when he saw Bilal lying on the earth with a huge boulder on his chest. He was deeply hurt to see Bilal like this. He turned to Ummayya and said, "How long are you going to torture this slave in your efforts to turn him away from Allah?"

"Be quiet, replied Ummayya, "You are the one who is the cause of his punishment; it is you who corrupted him."

"I did not corrupt him. I guided him to the Truth. I am prepared to buy him from you."

"So you want to buy him then? How much will you pay?"

"Five ounces of gold."

Ummayya agreed immediately, and so Abu Bakr bought Bilal for this amount.

"What," said Ummayya, "if I had refused to sell him except at a much higher price?"

"I would have paid even a hundred ounces."

Abu Bakr lifted the stone from Bilal's chest and helped him up and then slowly they both left the place. In the street, Bilal turned to Abu Bakr and said; "If you bought me for yourself, then you must keep me. But if you bought me for Allah's sake, then let me go, in the Name of Allah."

Abu Bakr replied, "You are free, Bilal."

The two men continued walking until they had reached the house of the Prophet. Abu Bakr told him all that had happened.

4   THE   FIRST   MUADHIN

From this time onwards, Bilal would accompany the Prophet,(may Allah bless him and grant him peace), assisting him in his work and learning about his message. When the Prophet ordered some of his companions to migrate to Madinah, Bilal was amongst them. He travelled at night in the company of Saad Abi Waqaas and Ammar Ibn Yasser. When the group arrived at Madinah, they were treated as brothers by the good people there, who welcomed lovingly all those who had emigrated in the way of Allah to their city. Even if they themselves were poor, the people of Madinah provided generous help for all those who came.

Bilal lived in Madinah in a state of agitation. He was longing to look again at the radiant face of his beloved Prophet. Every day he would go to the outskirts of the city to see if the Prophet was approaching, because he had heard that he was soon to emigrate to Madinah in the company of Abu Bakr As-Siddiq.

When that day finally arrived, Bilal was hardly able to contain his happiness, In Madinah, however, Bilal became quite ill, afflicted by the heat. He would recite poetry which expressed a yearning for Makkah:

"I wish I knew if I would be spending the night
In the valley of Adkher and Jaleel,
And if I will go one day to the water of Majanna,
And if Shafa and Tafeel will appear to me . . . "

These were all places in Makkah which Bilal used to know and see every day in his comings and goings. The poetry showed his love for the city in which he had lived for so long. It was there that he had suffered much hardship, but it was also the place where Allah had bestowed the blessings of Islam upon him.

Now that he was in Madinah, the first most important task undertaken by the Prophet,(may Allah bless him and grant him peace), was the building of the mosque at Qubba, after the direction of the Qibla had been redirected from Jerusalem to the Ka'aba.

One day, after the mosque had been constructed, the Prophet was sitting with his companions, discussing with them the best way of calling the Muslims to prayer. Some Muslims had told the Prophet that they were missing the congregational prayers because they did not know the timings of the prayer. One of the companions suggested:

"We should hoist a flag at the time of prayer - when the people see it they will tell each other." But this idea did not please the Prophet.

Someone else said: "We should light a fire - everyone will see it and come for prayer."

But someone called out, "That is the custom of the Magians."

"We could call on a horn," said someone.

"That is a Jewish custom."

"We can use a hand-bell," suggested someone else.

"That is a Christian custom."

The discussion continued amongst the Muslims and the Prophet,(may Allah bless him and grant him peace), and ended in the decision to make use of the hand-bell, to which the Prophet agreed, albeit grudgingly.

Abdullah Ibn Zaid, a Muslim who was present at the discussion, was troubled to see the Prophet in such a worried and reflective mood. He asked Allah to guide him and help him solve the problem of finding a fitting call to prayer.

When Abdullah Ibn Zaid Al-Ansari went home, his wife asked him: "Why are you not eating with us?"

He replied, "I cannot eat. I saw the Prophet of Allah today, worried about the question of the call to prayer."

Abdullah went to perform his ablutions, did two rakaats of prayer and settled down in a state of cleanliness and purity. While he was sleeping, Abdullah saw a man wearing green clothes. In his hand was a hand-bell.

Abdullah asked him, "Will you sell this bell?"

"What do you want to do with it?" the man asked.

"I want to use it to call the Muslims to prayer."

"Forget about the bell, I will tell you of a much better way."

"What is that?" asked Abdullah.

"Say: 'Allahu Akbar, Allahu Akbar. I bear witness that there is no god but Allah, I bear witness that there is no god but Allah. I bear witness that Muhammad is the Messenger of Allah, I bear witness that Muhammad is the Messenger of Allah. Come to prayer Come to prayer. Come to Success, Come to Success. Allah is the Greatest, Allah is the Greatest. There is no god but Allah."

The man in Abdullah's dream delivered the call to prayer in a strong, sweet voice from the roof of the mosque; then he sat down, then he rose and began to pray.

Abdullah awoke from his sleep in a state of great happiness and hurried to the Prophet to tell him this news. The Prophet, (may Allah bless him and grant him peace), told him to go and teach the call to Bilal, as he had the best voice of them all.

Umar also came to the Prophet and said, "O Messenger of Allah, I too had a similar dream to that of Abdullah Ibn Zaid."

The Prophet of Allah replied, "Allah be praised that this fact has been confirmed."

From this time onwards, Bilal would climb to the highest part of the mosque, to call people to the prayer; to call them to success. Bilal's delicate voice with its sweet melody had long been renowned amongst the people of Makkah. Even when he had been a slave of Ummayya, his songs and poetry had delighted everyone. Now his voice filled the streets of Madinah, and the words he used were the best he had ever uttered.

As Bilal's call to prayer in his beautiful voice resounded throughout the city, all the Muslims would hear him and rise from their sleep to hurry to the mosque to pray in the company of the Prophet, for the dawn prayers. Bilal, with the agreement of the Prophet, included the words, "Prayer is better than sleep, Prayer is better than sleep", in the early morning call to prayer. Thus Bilal was the first Muadhin of the Prophet, (may Allah bless him and grant him peace), in recognition of his beautiful voice and its clarity and perfection.

Now, whenever I hear the voice of a Muadhin calling us to pray, my mind goes back fourteen centuries, and I imagine Bilal Ibn Rabah, standing on the roof of the Qubba mosque, calling the people to·pray behind the Prophet, in his high pitched and delicate voice.

5   THE   JIHAD   WITH   THE   UNBELIEVERS

It was at Badr that the Muslims first came to blows with the tribe of the Qureish and war eventually broke out between the two armies. During the battle, the Muslims who had migrated to Madinah, remembered how the Qureish had maltreated and persecuted them and committed all kinds of vile deeds against them.

25

Bilal remembered Ummayya Ibn Khalaf and the treatment he had received at his hands and this made his blood boil. He hoped he would see Ummayya on the day, so that he could take his own revenge on him.

He would give him twice the measure which he himself had received. He began searching around on the battlefield for Ummayya, but could not find him anywhere. He promised himself that he would kill him if he saw him.

During the fight, the Muslims, who were heavily outnumbered, appealed to Allah for help, so He sent down 5,000 angels, who scattered the Qureish all over the place, filling with terror the hearts of those who disbelieved. Those of them who were able to flee, did so, and those who could not, waited to be taken into captivity.

Now, as luck would have it, Ummayya Ibn Khalaf was amongst those who had been unable to escape and was waiting quietly for the chains to be brought. Abdur Rahman Ibn Auf happened to pass by, and Ummayya called to out him, "O Abdur Rahman!"

Abdur Rahman turned to him and said, "Yes?"

"Do you need any more slaves? I will be better for you than those idiots you have with you."

Abdur Rahman agreed to take Ummayya and his son. He took their hands and set off in the direction of the

Prophet. On his way, he happened to pass by Bilal. When Bilal saw Ummayya, he rose from where he was sitting and hurried towards him, shouting, "It is the unbeliever, Ummayya Ibn Khalaf. There is no escape for you now!" He lifted his sword in order to kill him but was stopped by Abdur Rahman Ibn Auf, who said, "O Bilal, leave my slave alone."

Bilal replied, "There is no escape for him now!"

Bilal continued to circle around Ummayya and his son, but Abdur Rahman protected them both and told Bilal to leave them. Bilal however, shouted at the top of his voice, "O Helpers of Allah, here is the unbeliever, Ummayya Ibn Khalaf. There is no escape for him now!"

A group of the Ansar (the people of Madinah) came foreward and gathered around Ummayya, and someone hit out at Ummayya's son, killing him. Abdur Rahman told Ummayya, "Go and save yourself, I have no more need of you."

So Ummayya ran, followed closely by Bilal. When Bilal caught up with him, he lifted his sword high and brought it down over his former master. Ummayya fell to the ground, lifeless.

Looking down at the body of Ummayya, Bilal said' "There is nothing weaker than you now, O Ummayya."

Later he met Abdur Rahman Ibn Auf who said to him, "O Bilal, you have deprived me of my slave."

"May Allah grant you better than him." Bilal replied.

After having defeated the Qureish at Badr, the Muslims set about gathering the spoils and booty of war. It was the first time that they had the occasion to do so and they were confused how they should distribute it. It was at this point the the Prophet received the Revelation from Allah, saying:

"Know that whenever you aquire some booty, then for Allah is one fifth: for the Prophet and for relations and orphans and the poor and the wayfarers".

The Prophet of Allah divided the spoils, taking out one fifth for this purpose. He called Bilal and paid it to him. Bilal thus became the first Treasurer of the Trustworthy Prophet, (may Allah bless him and grant him peace). Now, whenever any poor or needy person came to the Prophet, he would send them to Bilal, to be fed and clothed.

One day, the Prophet went to see Bilal and found him saving a bag of dates. He asked Bilal what the matter was. "I am saving them for you and your guests," Bilal replied. The Prophet however, told him to spend with a free hand: "Do not fear any restraint from the Lord of the Throne."

28

Eventually, the Prophet entered Makkah triumphantly and victoriously, ten years after he had been forced to emigrate to Madinah. He walked around the Ka'aba

seven times; then he went with Bilal towards the door of the Ka'aba and found it closed. He asked for the key and was told that it was with Uthman Ibn Talha. He ordered it to be brought immediately. Uthman came to the Prophet of Allah and the Prophet said to him, "Bring me your keys Uthman, today is the day for Truth and the fulfillment of promises."

The Messenger of Allah, (may Allah bless him and grant him peace), then opened the door of the Ka'aba and entered it, accompanied only by Bilal Ibn Rabah, Usama Ibn Zaid and Uthman Ibn Talha. The Prophet prayed two rakaats and witnessed the angels who were present, and the vision of Ibrahim. Then he hit the idols with his stick and recited the Words of Allah:

"The Truth has come and the falsehood has been driven out; verily falsehood has been repudiated."

The Prophet then ordered Bilal to climb up onto the roof of the Ka'aba and to call the people to prayer. When the disbelievers saw him, they were utterly dumbstruck and began asking each other, "What does the slave think he is doing? How does he dare to climb the Sacred House, which no-one has ever done before?"

Harith Ibn Hisham, Sufyan Ibn Harb and Utab Ibn Asyad were sitting on one side of the Ka'aba when they saw Bilal on its roof. Utab said, "It is a good thing that my father did not hear of this, or he would have been really angry." He looked at Harith and said, " Do you see where that slave is climbing?"

"Leave him, if Allah is displeased with him, He will do something about it."

Then Bilal called out from the roof of the Ka'aba for the very first time: "Allah is the Greatest, Allah is the Greatest. I bear witness that there is no god but Allah, I bear witness that there is no god but Allah. I bear witness that Muhammad is the Messenger of Allah, I bear witness that Muhammad is the Messenger of Allah. Come to prayer, Come to prayer. Come to Success, Come to Success. Allah is the Greatest, Allah is the Greatest. There is no god but Allah."

Thus the first Adhan of the Muslims in Makkah resounded throughout the city, causing it to shake violently. It was as if the words were arrows, piercing the chests of the unbelievers that stood around the Ka'aba, amazed and wonderous. The sweet voice of Bilal, flowed through the streets of Makkah . . . Bilal, the weak slave who believed in Allah and who alone had been honoured by Him with the privilege of climbing on to the top of the Sacred House. It was an honour which even the noblemen of the tribe of the Qureish and their leaders had not been allowed.

Indeed, Bilal's voice resounded loudly in the ears of the leaders of the Qureish, and they were not able this time to hit him or torture him as they had done previously. Rather they themselves were now the prisoners of the Trustworthy Prophet, whom they had cast out of Makkah, and whose poor and oppressed followers they had sent away,(may Allah bless him and his family and his companions and grant them peace).

6   THE MARRIAGE OF BILAL

Bilal was sitting in his house one day, when his brother Abi Ruwaiha Al-Jumathi came to see him. Bilal stood up and embraced his brother and they both sat down together. Bilal asked his brother: "I hope you are well, by the Will of Allah."

"Praise be to Allah," replied Abi Ruwaiha. "I have come straight from the Yemen to talk to you about a very important matter."

"What is it?" asked Bilal.

"Well the reason I went there was to ask for the hand of one of their women in marriage."

"And what happened?" asked Bilal.

"I told them that I am from amongst the Arabs. They asked me about my tribe, from whom I am descended, about my lineage. Then I told them the truth, that I am an Abyssinian, born in Makkah, from the tribe of Bani Juma and that I am the brother of Bilal Ibn Rabah, the companion of the Prophet of Allah. They told me that if I brought you as proof of this, then they would certainly accept my marriage offer, So I have come to ask you to accompany me to the Yemen."

"I will have to ask the Prophet of Allah, then I will come with you." Bilal went to ask the Prophet if he could accompany his brother to Yemen and was give his approval. Bilal and his brother set off together. They arrived late at night and spent the night in the mosque. In the morning they set off for the house of the bride. Bilal sat with the leader of the tribe and told him:

"I am Bilal Ibn Rabah - and this is my brother. He is a bad tempered person. If you wish to accept him in marriage, then go ahead."

The leader of the tribe was amazed at Bilal's words and asked him. "How can you say that your brother is a bad tempered person, when he brought you here to eulogise him and praise him?"

There was, however, nothing for him to be astonished at, for this incident merely illustrated a significant aspect of the life and morals of Bilal. Bilal was indeed a truthful man, his tongue had no knowledge of lies or deceit and it was not his custom to cheat or be treacherous. Bilal had merely told the tribe what he knew to be the truth about his brother and revealed to them the weak characteristics of his personality. In the event, this truthful description proved to be more effective in impressing the tribe, than all the praise in the world. The outcome was that the tribe welcomed the marriage of Abi Ruwaiha.

After Bilal had settled the matter of his brother's wedding, he himself began to think about marrying. "Why should I not also marry?" he thought. "Marriage after all, is half of the life transaction."

Now Bilal began to wonder whom he should marry - from which tribe should she be? Finally Allah guided him in this matter, to the people of Hind. Bilal went to them and said:

"I am Bilal Ibn Rabah, companion of the Prophet of Allah, a slave from Abyssinia. I was astray and Allah guided me; I was a slave and Allah freed me. If you accept my offer of marriage, then praise be to Allah - and if you forbid me to marry, Allah is the Greatest."

They said to Bilal, "Wait a little until we ask the Prophet of Allah."

Bilal returned to Madinah. The days passed by. Finally the representatives of Hind came to see the Prophet and asked him: "We are from the Yemen. We have come to ask you about Bilal. He wishes to marry our sister and we told him to wait until we had asked you about him, and heard your opinion, O Prophet of Allah."

At this, the Holy Prophet, (may Allah bless him and grant him peace), smiled and said, "And who are you to ask about Bilal? He is a man of Paradise!"

The people of Hind were delighted by the Prophet's love for Bilal and his high opinion of him, and they married their sister to him. Bilal and his wife were very happy and Bilal was especially pleased to have fulfilled the injunctions of his religion.

One day Bilal returned from the night prayer to his house and sat next to his wife, telling her of the sayings of the Prophet and of the courtesies of Islam. His wife however, questioned one of the sayings and refused to believe it. This made Bilal very angry. He could hardly restrain his impatience and went out straight away to the Prophet, and told him what his wife was saying. The Prophet took Bilal's hand and went in the direction of his wife's house. The Prophet asked Bilal's wife, "Has Bilal offended you?"

"No," she replied.

"Perhaps you are angry with him?"

"No, he loves me greatly."

"What Bilal told you about me is true; Bilal does not lie. Do not anger Bilal - if you anger him, no works of yours will be accepted."

After the Prophet's kind words of advice, peace once again returned to the household of Bilal, and he and his wife lived together in serenity and perfect happiness.

7 THE DEATH OF THE PROPHET
(may Allah bless him and grant him peace)

Bilal accompanied the Prophet throughout his lifetime, fighting at his side in battle, struggling with him in times of conflict and spending periods of peace in worship and prayer. This pattern of life continued until the Holy Prophet, (may Allah bless him and grant him peace), passed away.

Bilal one day entered the room of the Prophet. He was lying on his bed for the last time. The tears flowed down from Bilal's eyes and he felt a deep sadness in his chest. He prayed and left for his house, deeply grieved. Thus the Prophet of Allah passed away - the Prophet, who had shown Bilal more affection than a mother gives her own child, and more fondness than a father shows his only son - and Bilal loved him greatly. He had later learned that it had been the Prophet who had told Abu Bakr to buy him and had asked him to let him pay some of the cost.

"Verily," thought Bilal, "you were the radiant moon and the glittering lamp who lighted the way for mankind from the darkness of life - I wonder how we are going to live after your light has gone . . . no . . . Allah forbid."

"The Prophet of Allah will remain alive throughout time through his noble example and his life which shall be a light for all people for all time. The Prophet of Allah will not die for as long as the Qur'an Al-Kareem remains, as long as Muslims carry on reading the Holy Qur'an, morning and evening; as long as the pure example of the Prophet and his noble life continues to be brought to the attention of mankind on occasions such as the Friday prayer and the Eid festivals, and at every prayer, everyday, every moment . . ."

Bilal was not able to sleep that night because of his grief at the passing away of his beloved Prophet and he stayed awake, hour after hour, until dawn began to appear on the horizon. He left for the mosque to call people to the Dawn prayers as was his daily practice. It was also Bilal's custom to pray to his Creator before calling the Adhan, asking Him to guide him to the right path and to piety and virtue and freedom from all want. He also used to ask Allah, to be surrounded by good, honest and trustworthy friends.

When the time for prayer came, Bilal raised his voice, in its melodious chant, increased in its awesomeness and loftiness by the stillness of the night.

"Allah is the Greatest, Allah is the Greatest. Allah is the

Greatest, Allah is the Greatest. I bear witness that there is no god but Allah, I bear witness that there is no god but Allah. I bear witness that . . ."

Bilal's voice began to falter, his tongue was unable to utter another word and the tears began to fall down from his eyes and trickle down his cheeks like falling rain . . .

It took a great effort on the part of Bilal to be able to control himself, and to be able to complete the Adhan in a low calm voice:

"I bear witness that Muhammad is the Messenger of Allah. I bear witness that Muhammad is the Messenger of Allah. Come to Prayer. . .Come to Prayer, Come to Success. . .Come to Success. Prayer is better than sleep ... Prayer is better than sleep. Allah is the Greatest. Allah is the Greatest. There is no god but Allah."

After the prayer, Bilal returned to his house thinking, "Truly in your death I feel a great loss, but this is Allah's decree which we cannot reverse and His order which we cannot change."

Bilal waited until the time for the midday prayer, then went out to the mosque. He found a corner in which he sat down, at a distance from the other people. When the time for the Adhan came, everyone listened out for the voice of Bilal. But Bilal did not raise his voice. This astonished everyone and they began to look for Bilal everywhere. A man found Bilal sitting alone in his corner and shouted to him: "The Adhan, O Bilal!"

"I will not give the Adhan after today," replied Bilal. "Let someone else give the Adhan."

Abu Bakr came forward, calling, "Where is Bilal?"

Bilal went towards him and said, "Here I am."

"The Adhan, O Bilal!"

"No," Bilal replied.

"But why?"

"If you had released me for yourself then you would have the right to make me do it, but if you released me for the sake of Allah, then let me go."

"I released you only for Allah," Abu Bakr replied.

"I will not give the Adhan for anyone after the Prophet of Allah," Bilal said.

Thus Bilal refused absolutely to give the Adhan for anyone after the Prophet, because of his total devotion to the Trustworthy Messenger, (may Allah bless him and grant him peace).

8   THE   SPREAD   OF   ISLAM

The time now came for the Muslims to choose the successor to the Prophet, as their leader. The agreed successor was Abu Bakr As-Siddiq, who had been, for many years, a close companion and friend of the Holy Prophet. One of the first tasks of Abu Bakr As-Siddiq as Khalif, was to organise the army of Usama Ibn Zaid, which the Holy Prophet had requested to prepare for war, shortly before his death, and to send it to the land of Syria.

Abu Bakr prepared the army. When the time for departure arrived, Usama waited at the head of his army for the Khalif to come and see them off, and to give them advice.

Abu Bakr arrived from afar on foot and when he drew closer, Usama made a move to dismount from his horse. Abu Bakr however, indicated to him not to do so. Usama said to him:

"O Successor of the Holy Prophet, please either let me dismount or climb up on a horse yourself."

But Abu Bakr simply replied, "No, do not dismount. I will not mount either. Why should I not get my feet dusty for the sake of Allah on this occasion, for it is a conquerer who for every step has 700 blessings and is elevated by 700 grades and 700 bad deeds are wiped away from his account."

Now while the two men were talking, Bilal approached them wearing battle clothing. When Abu Bakr saw him like this, he asked him, "And where are you off to, O Bilal?"

"I came to ask your permission to go to battle with the army of Usama."

"No Bilal, stay here with us."

"O Successor of the Holy Prophet, I have felt an emptiness since the passing of the Prophet of Allah and I thought that I would like to go to fight in the Holy War."

"Stay with us O Bilal, I have need of you here," Abu Bakr implored.

"O Successor of the Holy Prophet . . . I . . ."

"I implore you in the Name of Allah, O Bilal, and out of respect of me, don't go."

So Bilal agreed to remain behind, and Abu Bakr continued to give instructions about the campaign to Usama. The army finally set off, in the Name of Allah, confident and happy.

The days passed by and Bilal remained in Madinah, watching the army and its equipment on the way to the front and the soldiers who were conquering the world for Allah and spreading the message of the Holy Qur'an. From time to time, Bilal would hear the announcements of the victories of the Muslim armies in Syria and Iraq and whenever he heard good news, his heart would sometimes become heavy because he was unable to also participate in the conquests and the spreading of the message of Islam.

The fact was that Bilal was actually a very powerful soldier. A warrior spirit flowed in his veins; how he had fought and struggled in his time and how often he had participated in conquests with the Prophet of Allah. Bilal was about to go to Abu Bakr to ask him once again for permission to go to war, remembering that Allah had favoured those who fight over those who stay at home by one degree - and Bilal was not satisfied, ever, unless he was at the highest degree.

However, Bilal came to hear that Abu Bakr was ill, so he did not go to make his request. Abu Bakr,(may Allah be pleased with him).   died, and was succeeded by Umar Ibn Al-Kattab,(may Allah be pleased with him). Accordingly Bilal now went to Umar to ask for his permission to go to war.

41

Umar said to him: "Why don't you stay Bilal, with me, as you were with the Holy Prophet and with Abu Bakr?"

"I want to go to fight the Holy War, O Commander of the Faithful."

"If that is your wish Bilal. Where do you want to go?"

"I will meet up with Abi Ubaida in Syria," Bilal replied.

Go with the Blessings of Allah," said Umar.

So thus it was that Bilal was finally able to fulfil his wish. He travelled until he caught up with the armies of Abi Ubaida, where the Muslim armies had surrounded the Sacred Mosque in Jerusalem. The ruler of the city was however refusing to surrender until the Commander of the Faithful, Umar Ibn Al-Khattab, himself came. So Abi Ubaida sent a messenger to Umar informing him of this matter.

Umar sent back the reply to the leader of his armies to gather in a certain area before making their ascent to the Sacred Mosque. So Abi Ubaida, accompanied by Bilal and the other leaders, waited for the arrival of the Commander of the Faithful.

When Umar had arrived from Madinah, the time for the next prayer had arrived and the people asked Umar to order Bilal to call the Adhan. So Bilal stood up and raised his voice for the first time since the death of the Holy Prophet, (may Allah bless him and grant him peace).

Its sound aroused great sadness. Memories of the Beloved Prophet were rekindled amongst those gathered, to such an extent that many of the Companions began to cry, most of all Umar Ibn Al-Kattab. When the Prayer was over, Umar went to receive the keys of the Sacred Mosque.

9   THE DEATH OF BILAL

The days passed,and in the twentieth year after the Hijra, Bilal became seriously ill. His face became pale and his eyes clouded over. One day his wife asked him, "How are you feeling today?"

"Death is approaching," came the reply.

Then Bilal opened his eyes and said to her, "Tommorow I will meet the Beloved Muhammad and his Companions."

Then he repeated for the last time, the words he had first said to Abu Bakr when he was a slave, the words which he had repeated so often since then: "I bear witness that there is no god but Allah, and I bear witness that Muhammad is the Messenger of Allah.

Then he closed his eyes and his head fell to his chest and he breathed his last breath.

10   POSTFACE

عَنْ أَنَس قَالَ: قَالَ رَسُولُ اللّه
صَلَّى اللّهُ عَلَيْهِ وَ سَلَّمَ. مَنْ خَرَجَ
فِى طَلَبِ الْعِلْمِ فَهُوَ فِى سَبِيلِ اللّه
حَتَّى يَرْجِعَ

(التِّرمِذِىُّ وَ الدَّارِمُى)

It is reported by Anas that the Messenger of Allah,
(may Allah bless him and grant him peace) said;

'Whoever goes out to seek knowledge, is in Allah's path until he returns.'

(Tirmidhi and Darimi)

List of Islamic Words/concepts

أجل AJAL — the time appointed by ALLAH (SWT) for any event

الآخرة AL ĀKHIRAH — judgment; eternal consummation of judgment in Paradise or Hell

أخ 'AKH — (pl. IKHWAH, IKHWĀN) brother in faith

أذان ADHĀN — call to the supreme act of worship

الاسراء AL ISRĀ' — nocturnal journey of Muhammad (SAAS) to AL QUDS (Jerusalem) and return to Makkah

أسوة حسنة USWAH ḤASANAH — the good, normative example of the Prophet (SAAS) which is constitutive of the *sunnah*

ألله ALLÁH — the name of the divine majesty

أللهم ALLAHUMMA — the invocational form of ALLAH, used in worship and prayer

أمة UMMAH — the community as identified by its ideology, law, religion, and group consciousness, ethic and mores, culture and art

إمام IMĀM — community leader in religious as well as in lay matters

مجاهد MUJĀHID	(pl. MUJĀHIDŪN) those who practice JIHĀD
الجاهلية ALJAHILIYYAH	the order or regime in which the law of ALLAH (SWT) is not in force; pre-Islāmic Arabia
جهنم JAHANNAM	the eternal fire which is the ultimate recompense of the life of disobedience and sin
المجيب AL MUJĪB	a divine name, He Who responds favorably to prayer
حجاب ḤIJĀB	the covering of a Muslim woman; the Islamic style of dress for women
حجّ ḤAJJ	the fifth pillar of Islām, consisting of NIYYAH, IHRĀM, TAWĀF WUQŪF, ADḤĪYAH, and RAJM — acts performed at Makkah al Mukarramah on the ninth and tenth days of Dhū al Ḥijjah, the last month of the lunar year
حجّة ḤUJJAH	conclusive proof of the work, revelation or purpose of ALLAH (SWT)
حديث ḤADĪTH	(pl. AḤĀDITH) the verbalized form of a tradition of the Prophet Muḥammad (ṢAAS) constitutive of his SUNNAH

صلّى الله عليه وسلم — ṢALLĀ ALLAHU 'ALAYHI WA SALLAM.
May the peace and blessing of ALLAH be upon him (said whenever the name of the Prophet Muhammad (SAAS) is mentioned, or whenever he is referred to as the Prophet of ALLAH).

ماشاء الله — MA SHĀ'A ALLAH.
How wonderful are the works of ALLAH (said whenever one witnesses something good)!

إن شاء الله — IN SHĀ'A ALLAH.
If ALLAH wills it (said whenever one refers to the future).

السلام عليكم ورحمة الله — AL SALĀMU 'ALAYKUM WA RAḤMAH ALLAH.
May the blessing and mercy of ALLAH be upon you (said whenever a Muslim meets a Muslim; also whenever a Muslim enters a house or room).

وعليكم السلام ورحمة الله وبركاته — WA 'ALAYKUM AL SALĀM WA RAHMAH ALLAH WABARAKĀTUH.
May the blessing, mercy and the grace of God be upon you.

رضي الله عنه رضي الله عنهم — RADIYA ALLAHU 'ANHU (OR 'ANHUM)
May ALLAH be pleased with him (or with them) (said whenever a companion of the Prophet is mentioned by name).

عليه السلام عليهم السلام — ALAYH AL SALĀM OR ALAYHIM ALSALAM
Upon Him (or them) be the blessing (of Allah)

Rights of Parents

عَنِ الْمُغِيْرَةِ رَضِيَ اللهُ عَنْهُ قَالَ قَالَ رَسُوْلُ اللهِ صَلَّى اللهُ عَلَيْهِ وَسَلَّمَ : إِنَّ اللهَ حَرَّمَ عَلَيْكُمْ عُقُوْقَ الْأُمَّهَاتِ . (مُتَّفَقٌ عَلَيْهِ)

Al-Mughirah reported that Allah's Messenger (peace and blessings of Allah be upon him) said : Verily Allah forbade you to disobey the mothers. (Agreed upon)

عَنْ أَبِي هُرَيْرَةَ رَضِيَ اللهُ عَنْهُ قَالَ قَالَ رَجُلٌ يَارَسُوْلَ اللهِ صَلَّى اللهُ عَلَيْهِ وَسَلَّمَ : مَنْ أَحَقُّ بِحُسْنِ صَحَابَتِي؟ قَالَ : أُمُّكَ قَالَ : ثُمَّ مَنْ؟ قَالَ : أُمُّكَ قَالَ : ثُمَّ مَنْ؟ قَالَ : أُمُّكَ قَالَ ثُمَّ مَنْ؟ قَالَ أَبُوْكَ . (مُتَّفَقٌ عَلَيْهِ)

Abu Hurairah reported that a man asked the Messenger of Allah (peace and blessings of Allah be upon him) as to who amongst his near ones has the greatest right over him. He (the Holy Prophet) replied : "Your mother." He asked, "Then who is (next)?" He (the Holy Prophet) replied : "Your mother." He again asked, "Then who (is next)?" He (the Holy Prophet) replied : "Your mother." He asked : "Then who is (next)?" He (the Holy Prophet) replied : "Your father." Agreed upon)